# DON'T EAT THIS BOOK

BURP

HAHAHA

CRUNCH

YUM

CREATE IT,
MAKE IT YOURS...

## DAVID SINDEN & NikalaS CatLOW

( www.randomhousechildrens.co.uk )

DON'T EAT THIS BOOK
A RED FOX BOOK 978 1 849 41778 5
First published in Great Britain by Red Fox,
an imprint of Random House Children's Publishers UK
A Random House Group Company

This edition published 2012

5 7 9 10 8 6 4

Penguin Random House is committed to a sustainable future for
our business, our readers and our planet. This book is made from
Forest Stewardship Council® certified paper.

MIX
Paper from
responsible sources
FSC® C018179

Red Fox Books are published by
Random House Children's Publishers UK, 61–63 Uxbridge Road, London W5 5SA

www.**randomhousechildrens**.co.uk
www.**randomhouse**.co.uk

Addresses for companies within The Random House Group Limited can be found at:
www.randomhouse.co.uk/offices.htm

THE RANDOM HOUSE GROUP Limited Reg. No. 954009

A CIP catalogue record for this book is available from
the British Library.

Printed and bound in Great Britain by
Clays Ltd, St Ives plc

## LEGAL DISCLAIMER

HAVE FUN WITH THIS BOOK, BUT ALWAYS EXERCISE GOOD COMMON SENSE AND AVOID DOING ANYTHING DANGEROUS. SO DON'T BREAK A LEG BEING SILLY WITH IT THEN GO CRYING TO YOUR MUM. READING IT UNDERWATER IS A BAD IDEA TOO, AS IS COLLIDING WITH IT AT A HUNDRED MILES AN HOUR OR GLUING YOUR FACE TO IT. TRY NOT TO TRIP OVER IT, AND NEVER LET IT BURN AND SET FIRE TO YOUR HAIR. IT'S PROBABLY BEST TO WEAR A HELMET AND ELBOW PADS WHILE READING IT — JUST TO BE ON THE SAFE SIDE. (SERIOUSLY THOUGH, EXERCISE REASONABLE CARE FOR YOURSELF AND OTHERS WHILST USING THIS BOOK.)

# WHAT IS THIS BOOK?

This book is totally brilliant and a bit ridiculous. There's LOADS of stuff to do in it - WILD, creative stuff. It's fun, and you'll LOVE it!

## RULES FOR USING THIS BOOK:

RULE ONE - DON'T EAT THIS BOOK.

RULE TWO - THERE ARE NO MORE RULES.

RULE THREE - RULES SUCK.

## SO WHAT DO I DO?

Do absolutely anything you like, except eat it!
Each page is for you to mess with,
for your thoughts,
for your amusement.

This book is all about YOU.

# IDENTIFY YOURSELF

Fill this page with your name, as many times and in as many styles as you like.

Jaden

# A SELF-PORTRAIT

Draw OR paint a self-portrait wearing a *blindfold*.

# GET PHYSICAL

Be daring with this book. If you want to tear something out, tear it out; don't worry about what's on the other side of the page – it's OK, it's **THAT** sort of book! If you want to stick something in, stick it in. Draw what you want. Scribble what you want. Write what you want. Fill it with ideas, colour and noise. Take it everywhere, show everyone and share it if you want.

## TO LOOSEN UP, TRY THESE THINGS:
See how good they feel!

CLOSE THE BOOK. DRUM ON IT. WRITE YOUR NAME ON THE COVER AND CHANT REPEATEDLY: 'THIS BOOK IS MINE, ALL MINE – I CAN DO WHAT I WANT!'

Sure, no.

ADD COLOUR

WIPE JAM, TOOTHPASTE OR ANYTHING HERE:

Scribble outside the dotted lines. k!

Rip this bit off and throw it away. (Don't worry about what's on the back.)

Tape or glue an object here:

CAN YOU BALANCE THIS BOOK ON THE TIP OF ONE FINGER? CAN YOU SPIN IT?

No.

# squish things HERE...

Can you decorate this page with stains and splats?
Create by squishing peas, gum and berries – any
other ideas?

# CAN YOU
# SQUEEZE YOUR BODY THROUGH
# THIS PAGE?

Cut along the lines. | Unfold it – hey presto!

Draw a picture of someone you would like to slap, but wouldn't. **SLAP IT.**

Take this book outside and create a picture on these pages by applying colour or mud with bouncing balls: rubber balls, tennis balls, footballs — you choose!

# REMOVE THIS PAGE
## BIT BY BIT
### USING ONLY
#### A HOLE PUNCH.

Use the bits to decorate the front cover.

# FOLD THIS PAGE

# IN HALF AS MANY

## TIMES AS YOU CAN.

Can you do seven folds?

# MAKE THIS STRIPY

This page is for stripes: coloured stripes, black stripes, textured stripes, fat stripes, all the same stripes, or every stripe different — you choose!

# PRETEND THIS BOOK IS ATTACKING YOU

... AND SEE IF ANYONE NOTICES!

# THE LA LA SONG

Finish writing the 'La la' song – the song that gets on everyone's nerves. Sing it until people can take no more.

La la la la la . . .

Create an energetic image using rubber bands.
Dip them in paint and fire them at these pages.
Stretch them! Ping them! Or glue them on!

FO SHIZZLE!

Bling these pages using tin foil, metallic pens, paperclips, staples, glitter, etc.

**YOU** CREATE IN THIS DIRECTION.
Use an unusual drawing tool, such as a
borrowed lipstick or eyebrow pencil.

**YOUR FRIEND** CREATES IN THIS DIRECTION.
Add as many colours to the picture as you can.

# CAN YOU READ THIS?

W
HE
NYO
UCONC
ENTRATET
OREADTHISYO
USTARTTOSQUIN
TANDWHENYOUSTARTSQUI
NTINGITLOOKSLIKEYOUARECONSTIPATED

Here's a prune for you!

KEEP THIS PAGE IN THE TOILET TO SCRIBBLE ON
OR IN CASE YOU RUN OUT OF TOILET PAPER...

# CORRECT ✓ THIS

Can you correct these famous words of wisdom?

A BIRD IN THE HAND IS WORTH TWO IN THE TOILET
DON'T COUNT YOUR TOILETS BEFORE THEY HATCH
THE BIGGER THEY ARE, THE HARDER THEY TOILET
DON'T BITE OFF MORE THAN YOU CAN TOILET
A FOOL AND HIS TOILET ARE EASILY PARTED
NEVER BITE THE TOILET THAT FEEDS YOU
YOU CAN'T JUDGE A TOILET BY ITS COVER
DON'T LOOK A GIFT HORSE IN THE TOILET
DON'T PUT ALL YOUR EGGS IN ONE TOILET
BETWEEN A TOILET AND A HARD PLACE
A LEOPARD CAN'T CHANGE HIS TOILET
TOILETS SPEAK LOUDER THAN WORDS
WEAR YOUR HEART ON YOUR TOILET
LET THE CAT OUT OF THE TOILET
DON'T CRY OVER SPILT TOILETS
CURIOSITY KILLED THE TOILET
BARKING UP THE WRONG TOILET
A TASTE OF YOUR OWN TOILET
RAINING CATS AND TOILETS
COUNT YOUR LUCKY TOILETS
YOU ARE WHAT YOU TOILET
WATER UNDER THE TOILET

AS SICK AS A TOILET
SAVED BY THE TOILET
OVER MY DEAD TOILET
A CHIP ON YOUR TOILET
NEW KID ON THE TOILET
IT TAKES TWO TO TOILET
THE ICING ON THE TOILET
LET SLEEPING TOILETS LIE
THE BALL IS IN YOUR TOILET
HIT THE TOILET ON THE HEAD

# MAKE THIS BEASTLY

Caractinois

'It had the head of one creature, the body
of another, and the legs of a third!'
Add special features such as tentacles, horns,
wings, whatever. Name your beast.

WRITE A SECRET OVER AND OVER UNTIL
NO ONE CAN READ IT.

# Psychedelic poop

Imagine a parrot that poops in bright colours. How would this page look if it had been left below the parrot's perch?

# THROW THINGS AT YOUR WALL

## AT YOUR WALL

GRAFFITI IT

SHOUT USING ANY PAGE AS A MEGAPHONE.
THINGS TO SHOUT MIGHT INCLUDE:

'Headlice, headlice. Come and get your headlice!' (While scratching.)

'Get out of my personal space!'

'Everybody breakdance!'

'Look there's . . . (someone famous)!'

'I HAVE RABIES!' (With toothpaste round your mouth.)

'Will you be my fwiend?'

'Iced ink.'

'Move away from the vehicle!'

'Hoof hearted.'

'It wasn't me.'

'Stay off my property!'

'Hands up who's wearing clean underwear?'

OR YODEL, OR GARGLE, OR BURP.

SHOUT THIS

Draw here by holding a pen or paintbrush still, and moving the book instead.

MOVE
THIS BOOK

CREATE A...

# RAnSOm
# nOTe

IF U WANT BABY
BACK PAYNE.

£10000000!

C10TEN MILLION
POUNDS!

WHAT WOULD THIS
PAGE LOOK LIKE
IF IT HAD BEEN
USED AS A

# FLY
# SWATTER?

Try to scratch through this page
using only your fingers.

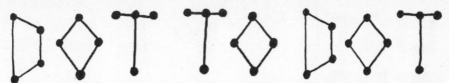

# DOT TO DOT

Join the dots in any order. Change colour and join them again in a new order. Do this over and over to create a design. Fill in any shapes you wish.

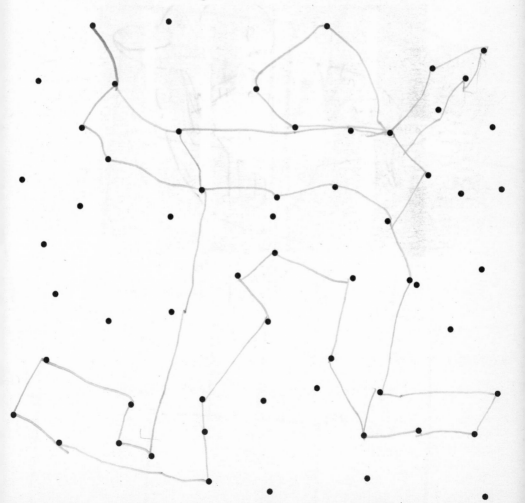

# LIST THIS

**PETS YOU'VE HAD OR WANT:**

Mini Pig
Pug

**YOUR BEST QUALITIES AND SKILLS:**

Football
Comedy /
being funny

**YOUR TOP TEN SONGS:**

Break my mind
and... dunno?

**THINGS YOU GOT INTO TROUBLE FOR:**

Talking
Fighting

**BOOKS YOU'VE READ:**

all!

**COUNTRIES YOU'VE VISITED:**

India....
T_T

**PLACES YOU'VE BEEN SICK:**

England
India

**PEOPLE YOU'VE KISSED:**

Mom

**YOUR FEARS:**
hights

**PEOPLE YOU ADMIRE:**
No1...

**YOUR FUTURE PLANS:**
nPug
gamemaker
Millionair
Billionair

**LOCATIONS OF THE MOLES ON YOUR BODY:**
None!

**YOUR FRIENDS:**
Radsan
tej
Zayan.S
T.H
Roiloll
Talby
**Anari**
(Adam)

**CONTENTS OF YOUR BEDROOM:**
?

**THINGS THAT ANNOY YOU:**
HADI

**INJURIES YOU'VE HAD:**
?Countless

DRAW HOW YOU WOULD LOOK
IF YOU WERE A DOG.

# A MOUSTACHE A DAY,
# FOR A WEEK.

Refine them. Design your own. Try them on.

# DRAW AROUND ROUND THINGS.

Find round objects. Draw around them lots of times
to create a pattern. Colour where they overlap.

# THIS ISN'T A LETTER L

It's part of something else. **YOU** decide what it is.

# THIS IS THE
# BOGEYMAN

What does he look like?

Use this page to let out your anger. Vent it here: write your thoughts, say the things you want to say but shouldn't. Draw your anger, then scribble it out, erase it. See how much better you feel!

# "🦟" BITE THIS 🦇

Add mosquito bites or vampire bites.
Draw how they look, make holes – attack!

PLEASE BE GENTLE!

# DRAW A
# HEADACHE

On these pages, create a big picture of
what a headache feels like.

# USE THIS BOOK TO
## ANNOY
## SOMEONE

If someone touches it, 'tut' loudly, then spray it with disinfectant.

Keep opening it and peering inside saying, 'Are you OK in there?'

Give it to someone and ask them to find the idiot page.

Act as if you're reading it and, each time you turn a page, do the following: laugh hysterically, snort, scream 'AAARGH! MY EYES!', then pretend to get an electric shock.

Show it to someone, frown, then whisper in a ghostly voice, 'Death by paper cuts.'

Pretend it weighs too much and keep dropping it. Then fall down as you try to pick it up.

Make explosion noises when anyone goes near it.

Every time someone speaks, slam the book shut and say, 'Well, that's that then!'

Leave it in the way. When someone goes to pick it up, say, 'Hey, that's mine!'

Stand next to someone and fan the air with it. Say to them, 'Did you have to do that?'

Sit at your desk with it, chuckling. When someone comes to see, ask them if they have an appointment.

Read it using binoculars. When someone quizzes you, reply, 'Aye aye, Captain,' to anything they say.

Leaf through it, sniffing each page and mumbling, 'Mmm, bananas.'

# THIS IS A COMIC

Add your own words.

Add your own words and pictures.

 # IS THIS RIDICULOUS SUPERHERO **?**

Cut out a picture of someone you don't know from a magazine. Paste it here. Invent a ridiculous superhero identity for them.

**SUPERHERO NAME:**
CAPTAIN POOPY PANTS!

**SUPER POWERS:**
POOPY Powers

**WEAKNESS:**
TOILET PAPER

**ENEMY'S NAME:**
LOOMGOO

**CATCHPHRASE:** PREPARE TO GET...

FLUSHED!

MAKE **THIS** PAGE SCARY.

# A BATTLE

Add smells to stink up these cheesy socks and perfume these flowers.

# OF SMELLS

Which smell is stronger?

# WHAT ARE THEY ?

Add your own secret surprises to these pages: stains, smears, gunge, fluff, sweets, toys, cake, anything! Challenge a friend to guess what they are or where you found them.

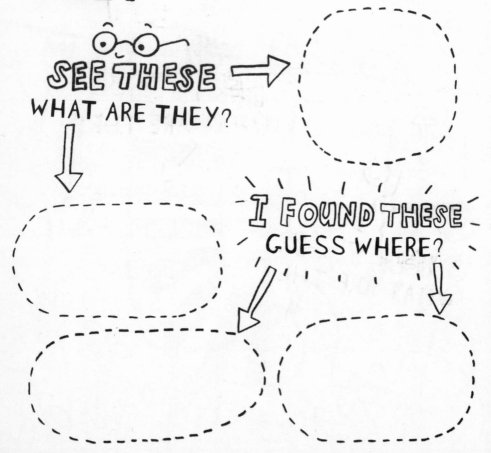

SEE THESE

WHAT ARE THEY?

I FOUND THESE

GUESS WHERE?

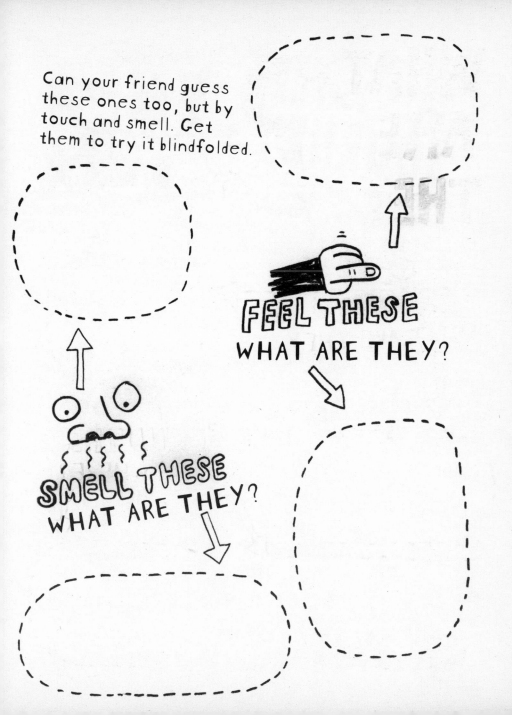

Can your friend guess these ones too, but by touch and smell. Get them to try it blindfolded.

FEEL THESE
WHAT ARE THEY?

SMELL THESE
WHAT ARE THEY?

# THIS IS FOR JOURNEYS

ARE WE NEARLY THERE YET?

This is like eye spy, but better. Which of the things below can you spot, hear or feel on your journey? Circle them as you go. On your next journey, circle them in a different colour.

GENUINE SNEEZE

STRIPY SOCKS

OLD MAN

SOMETHING STICKY

LAUGHTER

WORDS IN DIRT

SOMEONE DANCING

SQUEAKING SOUND

RED SQUARE

TOMATO

CLOUD THE SHAPE OF A FISH

YELLOW TRUCK

HORSE

GREEN CIRCLE

BOREDOM

AN IDIOT

SMELL OF BURGERS

GLASS BUILDING

CRYING CHILD

WASHING ON A LINE

MASSIVE TREE

WHITE SHOES

BLUE LIQUID

CROSS PARENT

DOG'S TONGUE

WINGS

PURPLE CAR

A BEEPING SOUND

SPOTTY BAG

WALKING FLY

BILLBOARD FOR A MOVIE

RIDERLESS BIKE

BLUE SPOTS

ARCHED WINDOW

SKATEBOARD

BLACK CAT

ORANGE T-SHIRT

BAD SMELL

THIS PAGE IS FOR . . .
bubble WRITING

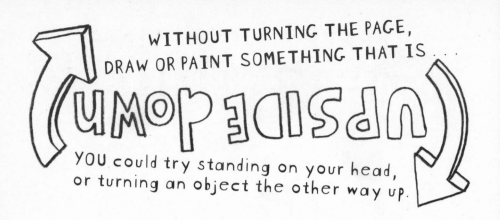

WITHOUT TURNING THE PAGE,
DRAW OR PAINT SOMETHING THAT IS . . .

⌒UPSIDE down⌒

YOU could try standing on your head,
or turning an object the other way up.

# LEAVE A SURPRISING MESSAGE ON THIS PAGE.

## PIN IT SOMEWHERE UNEXPECTED FOR SOMEONE TO FIND.

MAKE A TRAIL OF ARROWS TO YOUR MESSAGE.

WATCH QUIETLY TO SEE IF ANYONE FOLLOWS THEM.

# ADOPT

## THIS →

## AS YOUR PET

Staple some wool, fluff or hair to this book, and stick some eyes on it. Attach a lead to it. Give it a name and adopt it as your pet.

Take it for walks.
Teach it tricks. Feed it.

Record the number of weird looks you get from passers-by here:

# DRIP ON THIS

Drip paint onto these pages. Make a picture in 'plops' and in 'splats'.

# The LONG Distance PAGE

**HOW FAR CAN YOU MAKE THIS PAGE GO, AND STILL GET IT BACK AGAIN?**

You could try doing these:

1) Flying it as a paper aeroplane.

2) Scrunching it into a ball and throwing it.

3) Tearing it into strips and taping them end to end.

4) Tying it to a kite.

5) Posting it to friend or relative, kindly asking them to post it back with proof of where it's been.

WE HAVE LIFT OFF!

RECORD WHAT HAPPENS HERE:

Take a small, unimportant object: an eraser, a pen lid, a paperclip, etc. Examine it closely — use a magnifying glass if you wish. Draw a bit of it to fill this whole page. Make it important.

# PATTERN THESE **PANTS**.

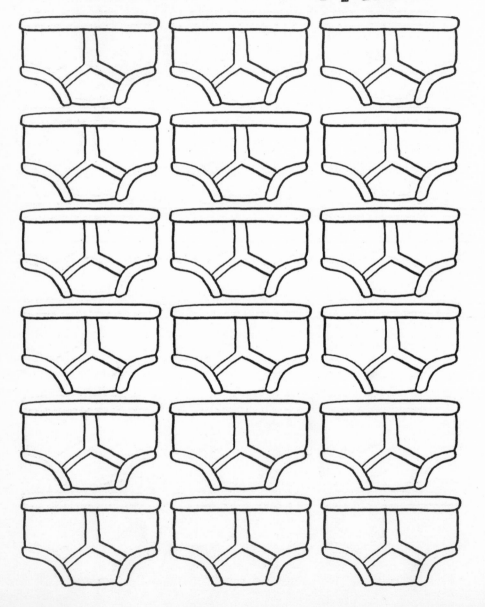

# MAKE EVERY PAIR DIFFERENT.

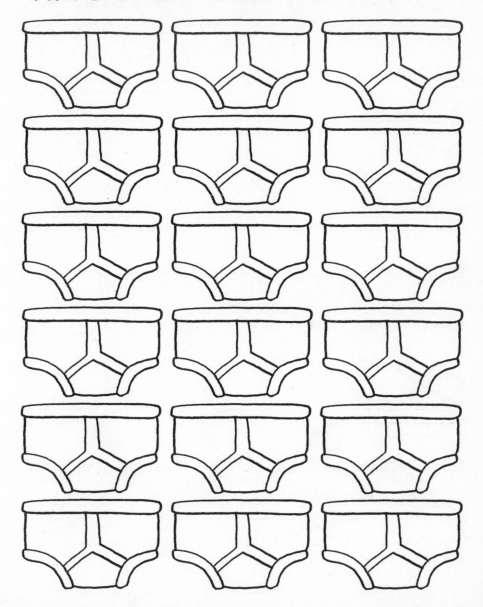

Take the book outside. Drop or toss a pen or crayon, and try to land it on these pages to make a mark. Can you draw from far away? Make a pattern from your marks, add scoring areas if you wish, or challenge a friend to a draw-off. Make sure there's no one in the way when you throw.

# FEEL THIS

This is a page to be enjoyed by your fingers, not your eyes. Gather together textures, including fabrics, and glue them on. Cover the page with them.

OOOH, FLUFFY!

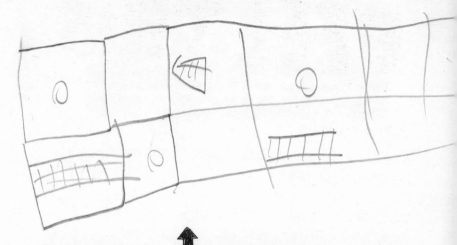

Look UP and draw what you see.

**STAND SOMEWHERE YOU'VE NEVER STOOD BEFORE...**

Look DOWN and draw what you see.

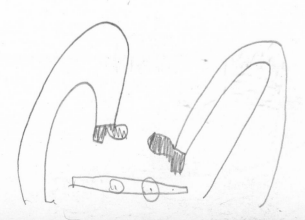

# DRIVE THIS

Close your eyes and race round this circuit with a pen, pencil or paintbrush. Time yourself – there's a five-second penalty if you go off track. Switch tools or colours and race again to improve your lap times, or challenge a friend. Create racing art.

# Make These Up

Here are some made-up words and their meanings.
Add some more of your own.

| WORD | MEANING |
|---|---|
| JAMSTEWING | Wearing your socks for weeks at a time. |
| HANDROID | Someone is who is always putting their hand up in class. |
| CRIGGLING | Giggling and crying at the same time, such as when being tickled. |
| BEDCRUSTER | Someone who avoids having a bath, and goes to bed muddy. |
| CRUMGE | What you find left at the bottom of the mug after a dunked biscuit falls into your tea. |
| ELATIONSHIP | Knowing someone only via email or on a social network. |
| SNUDGE | The mark left on a window after you've pressed your nose up against it. |
| MOLD | Someone old that looks like a mom. |
| FARAT | Someone far away that looks fat |
|  |  |
|  |  |

# WHAT'S PUZZLING YOU?

What could be tricky to put back together?
Draw something confusing. Cut it out.

# ROLL ON THIS

## ROLL A COIN TO SCORE!

30 POINTS

20 POINTS

50 POINTS

40 POINTS

10 POINTS

# COLOUR IT!

Try flipping the coin! Try tiddlywinks!

# BRUSH THIS

Swap your paintbrush for another kind of brush: an old toothbrush, nailbrush, hairbrush or even a broom. Use it to make a picture with movement in it by brushing paint on in different directions.

# SHAPE
## SHIFTERS
Using only the shapes below,
what can you design?

# 15 seconds...GO!

Draw each thing below as many times as you can in fifteen seconds. Challenge a friend to try — who can draw the most? Colour this page afterwards.

**The letter X**

**The letter S**

**The number 8**

**Lightning bolts**

**Circles**

**Spirals**

**String**

**Worms**

**Sheep**

**Eyes**

TIME'S UP!

# question this?

Make up your own ridiculous questions to these answers:

## QUESTIONS

1 Second +0 = ?

W.hale is?

Some 1 dumb?

Michael Mad! is?

liek the sloor?

£7,613,755 +£1?

boogers?

Comedian?

My socks

## ANSWERS

One second.

It's massive!

My friend Riaz
THEIR NAME

Incredibly annoying.

NEVER!

£7,613,756.

Gross.

ME!

Old and stinky.

 THIS

What would this page look like
if it had a disease?

# TWIST THIS

Can you say these tongue twisters fast,
over and over?

'FRESHLY FRIED FISH'    'KNAPSACK STRAP SHOP'

'STUPID SUPERSTITION!'    'A PROPER COPPER COFFEE POT'

'A CHEAP SHIP TRIP'    'FLASH MESSAGE!'

'FREDDY THRUSH FLIES THROUGH THICK FOG.'

'MUCH MASHED MUSHROOM'    'IRISH WRISTWATCH'

'CECILY THOUGHT SICILY LESS THISTLY THAN THESSALY.'

'SEVENTEEN SLIMY SLUGS IN SATIN SUNBONNETS
SAT SINGING SHORT SAD SONGS.'

'WILLIE'S WOODEN WHISTLE WOULDN'T WHISTLE.'

'MANY AN ANEMONE SEES AN ENEMY ANEMONE.'

'WHICH WITCH WINDS WHITE WEASEL WOOL WELL?'

'JUST THINK, THAT SPHINX HAS A SPHINCTER THAT STINKS!'

'GOOD GARGOYLE BLOOD, BAD GARGOYLE BLOOD.'

'FAT FROGS FLYING PAST FAST.'    'GREEK GRAPES'

'INCHWORMS ITCHING'    'UNIQUE NEW YORK'

'THREE FREE THROWS'

# ANIMATE THIS

Hold the book and flick
**JUST THIS PAGE** back and forth.
Remember to add your own sound effects!

HOLD
PAGE
HERE

# MAKE THIS RUNNY

Run paint down this page in different colours.
Let it dry. Add more.

# WARNING
# DON'T
# EVER
# TURN
# TO THE NEXT page

SKIP FORWARDS TWO PAGES!

# PUNISHMENT:
# COUNT THESE

## HOW MANY?

- Black squares ......
- Triangles ......
- White squares ......
- Black hearts ......
- White things ......
- Semicircles ......
- All things ......

Colour these pages when you've served your punishment.

# DON'T EVER TURN BACK TO THE PAGE BEFORE

How would this page look if it was a tissue
and you had blown your nose on it?

Make a poster for something imaginary or silly that
you've lost, e.g. a pet insect, a ghost, a smell or
your voice. Offer a reward asking people to find it.

# TATTOO
## THIS

Draw how your tattoo would look if you had one.

Where would it be?

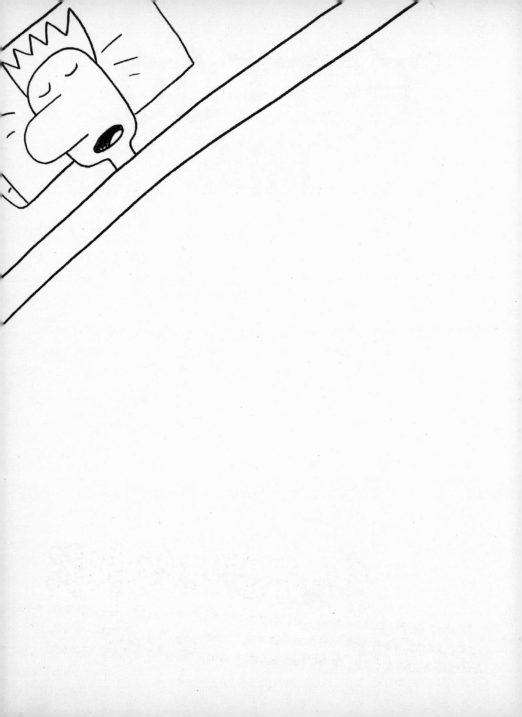

# PATCHWORK

Make a patchwork quilt on these pages. Glue on squares from plastic bags, packaging, junk mail, cloths and fabric - but not your mum's best dress!

# ASK this

ATTACH THIS BOOK TO A CLIPBOARD TO MAKE YOU LOOK IMPORTANT. SEE IF ANYONE CAN ANSWER THESE QUESTIONS AND ANY MORE YOU HAVE.

1. What's the opposite of opposite?

2. How long is a piece of string?

3. Who DID let the dogs out?

4. How fast is fast food?

5. Why did the chicken cross the road?

6. What disease did cured ham have?

7. Do people yawn in their sleep?

8. What was the best thing BEFORE sliced bread?

9. If you try to fail, and succeed, which have you done?

10. Can I borrow your car?

DRAW A PICTURE
WITHOUT TAKING YOUR
PEN OFF THE PAGE.

BETWEEN THESE PAGES

TO SANDWICH IT FOR EVER.

# MOUTHS I FOUND

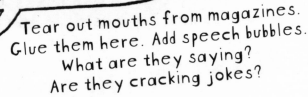

TALKING

Tear out mouths from magazines.
Glue them here. Add speech bubbles.
What are they saying?
Are they cracking jokes?

# EYES I FOUND LOOKING

Tear out eyes from magazines. Glue them here.
Add something unusual for them to look at.

Glue cereal onto this page.
Add images from the cereal box, and even spots
of milk if you wish — this is breakfast art.

# CHOOSE YOUR NAME

Rename yourself.
Choose one from each column:

| FIRST NAME | MIDDLE NAME | LAST NAME |
|---|---|---|
| Captain | Sparrow | Skullhead |
| DJ | Cool J | Iron fist |
| Emperor | Blind | Blurgh! |
| Blind | Mac | Chicken plucker |
| JZBC | Jelly-legs | The First |
| One-eyed | Pepper | The Invincible |
| No-pants | Bigfoot | Splatit |
| Cool | Vlad | Hornetsnest |
| Agent | Willy | McPants |
| Mad | Humungous | Wacko |
| Luscious | G-Ride | TV |
| Professor | Bling | of Everything |
| Big | Pants | Sidebottom |
| Major | Blind | Von Winkle |
| King | Burger | Power |
| Nefertiti | Wobbling | Star |
| Princess | Hairy | Headrot |
| Officer | Brains | Umbrella |
| Xerxes | Thor | The Second |
| Lord | Wizz | Pox |
| MC | The Man | Thunderthighs |
| Doctor | Wriggler | Wallywilly |

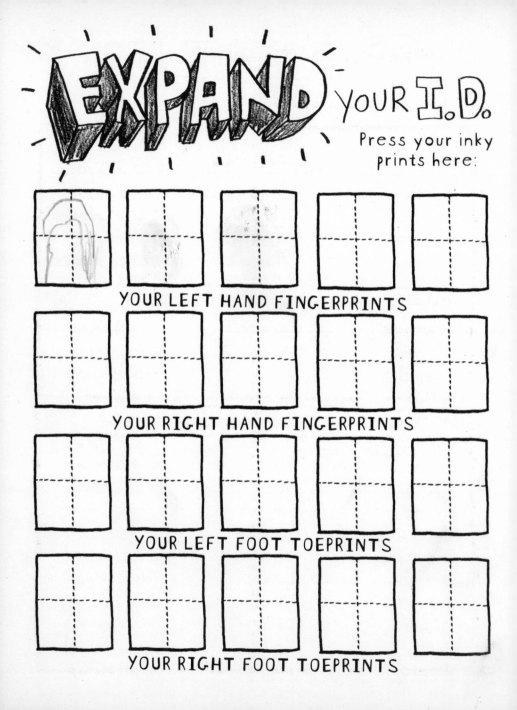

Pick one of your fingerprints or toeprints
and blow it up to enlarge the pattern in it.
Use the grid to help. Add colour if you want.

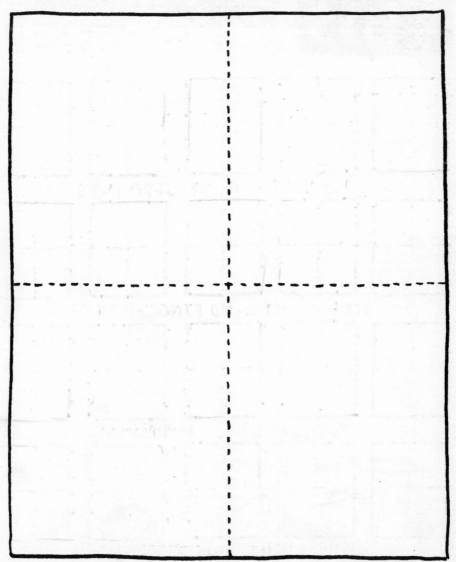

**BOX THIS**

Divide this page into boxes.
Divide some of those boxes
into more boxes. Fill boxes.
Stack boxes.

Who?

THIS IS

# OUT OF
# ORDER

Make it out of order.

# MEND THIS

How would this page look if it had been attacked by sharks, then been stitched back together in hospital?

# ALPHABET COLLECT

Collect a bit of something beginning with each letter and glue it here. If you can't find it, draw it.

| A | B | C | D | E |
|---|---|---|---|---|
| F | G | H | I | J |
| K | L | M | N | O |
| P | Q | R | S | T |
| U | V | W | X | Y |
| | | | | Z |

Same as H 15679 111

9994X5000

7         -6  12 34567

×2

=            ⌐⌐  9611176=

=           ⌐⌐

14          └┘

5

+20

# NUM3ER TH15

Think of a number between 1 and 10.
Times it by 2. Take away 5. Add 20. Take away 6.
Mulitipy it by 1.45782939. Divide it by 0. Give up.
Create a picture by filling this page with numbers.

# SECRETLY SELLOTAPE A STATEMENT SOMEWHERE.

How would this page look if snails slid across it?
Add your own slime trails, or leave outside with
lettuce on it to attract some for real.

# PUSH YOUR BIKE

MAKE MARKS WITH ITS WET AND MUDDY TYRES.

# ACROSS HERE

BEST DONE OUTDOORS IN THE GARDEN.

# HAND THESE OUT . . .

The person now holding this is a
.....Fat.........

HI!

fancies **YOU**
Hah

THIS ENTITLES YOU
TO NOTHING. PLEASE
COLLECT IT AT 3.30pm

**PLEASE LOOK
AFTER THIS.**

HA!

I COUGHED
ON **THIS**.

THE ANSWER IS
.....0..............

YOU'VE WON
A FREE GIFT!
**How to claim your gift:**
Go to the end of the road, wave your arms, shout 'I want
my free gift!', cry, do a robot dance – are you still reading?
Then write to the queen and say please could she send you
a corgi dog. Your free gift is inside it. Wait for it to do one.

**YOU** fancy
.....anut.........

Write or draw some of your own.

# SPIN AND GET DIZZY

## NOW TRY TO DRAW STRAIGHT LINES.

Do this where there is lots of space
and you won't bump into anything.

# HA HA BONK

Draw lines pairing each joke with its correct punchline. Colour the shapes you make. Find the rogue punchline — there's one extra!

In their sleevies.

No idea.

What did one string say to the other?

Who was in the toilet with Tigger?

What do you call a hippy's wife?

Why do birds fly south in the winter?

I'm a frayed knot!

What do you call cheese that's not yours?

Why is six scared of seven?

Where you left it.

Because pepper makes them sneeze!

Burple.

Invisible bananas!

Pooh.

A carrot.

What kind of ears do trains have?

Between you and me, it smells.

Why did the squirrel cross the road?

E-clipse it!

What colour is a burp?

Mississippi.

Because seven eight nine.

A ewe turn.

Why do fish live in salt water?

Why did the boy stare at the orange juice?

Where do you find a one-legged dog?

What's orange and sounds like a parrot?

To a retail store.

How do you kill a circus?

What do you call a deer with no eyes?

Engineers.

Nacho cheese.

What was the sheep doing in the car?

What did one eye say to the other?

To show his girlfriend he had guts.

Go straight for the juggler.

Because it's too far to walk!

Because it said concentrate.

Where does a cat go if it hurts its tail?

Where do generals keep their armies?

How does the moon cut his hair?

# FOOD ART

Rather than wipe your jam knife on a cloth, wipe it on these pages. Perhaps add the last scrapings of Marmite from the jar. Paint and collage with food scraps that are normally thrown away: fruit and vegetable peel, egg shells, burnt toast, gravy leftovers. It's food art. It won't last for ever – it may go mouldy and shrivel up. Take photos to record it changing before you have to throw it away.

# emotions

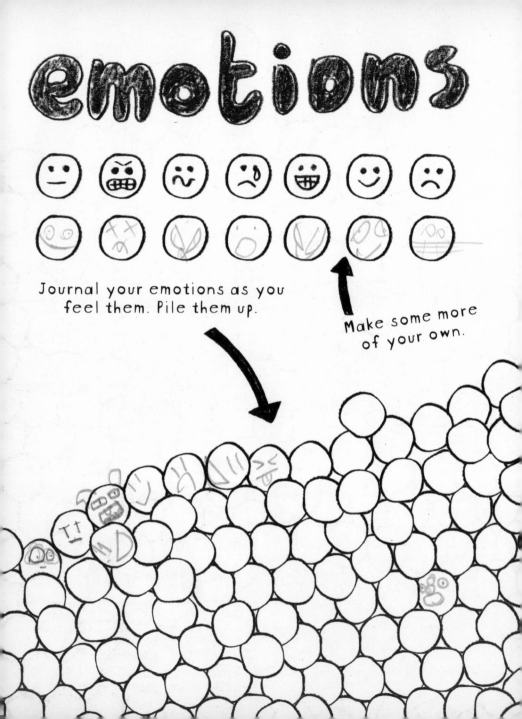

Journal your emotions as you feel them. Pile them up.

Make some more of your own.

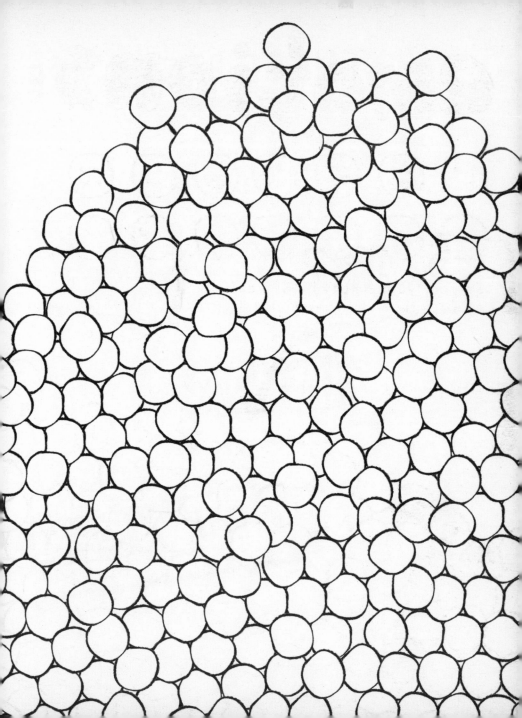

THESE PAGES ARE

START

A WAR

BETWEEN

A BATTLEFIELD . . .

Colour this page.
Tear into tiny pieces. Celebrate!

# THIS TICKLES

Make this page as tickly as you can.
Add feathers or poke through wiggling fingers.
Tickle someone with it.

JOIN IN: CREATE ASTEROIDS!

# SWAP THIS

Sign this page with your name to identify it.
Then swap it with your friend for the same page
of their book, and tape theirs here – they will
need a copy of this book too!

Jaden . . . . . . . . . . . . . . . . . . . . . . . . . . . .

Add your
head.

Add your
friend's head.

Fill this with TRIANGLES

Any way you like.

# THINGS YOU LIKE

monsters     animations

mcdonalds
or subway

football

bugs

Stack things you like here: in words and pictures.
Decorate them joyfully.

# THINGS YOU DON'T LIKE

Clowns

pollen

x-tra teeth

heights

agtish

wasps!

Stack things you don't like here: in words and pictures.
Splatter them with colours you hate.

DAUB THICK WET PAINT

ON THIS PAGE, THEN CLOSE

THE BOOK TO MAKE A  PRINT

When your print is dry, give it eyes, arms and legs.

Probably wont work

# GO DOTTY

Create a picture from just dots — lots of dots!

# WOULD YOU RATHER?

○ Sneeze at the end of every sentence?
○ Squeak when you speak?

○ Be armour-plated?
○ Be fireproof?

○ Have ears made of cheese?
○ Always stink of onions?

○ Your parents still dress you as a baby?
○ Your teacher is now dating your mum?

○ Never eat a burger again?
○ Never eat ice cream again?

○ Be able to fly?
○ Be able to read minds?

○ Have a lifelong nosebleed?
○ Have lifelong hiccups?

○ Eat someone else's bogey?
○ Eat someone else's earwax?

○ Have donkey ears?
○ Have fish eyes?

○ Come top of the class?
○ Hold the world record for juggling?

○ Be the richest person in the world?
○ Be the best-looking person in the world?

○ Fight a bear?
○ Fight a lion?

○ Have a beard full of maggots?
○ Have hair crawling with spiders?

# WANTED

NAME .R.laz.....................

CRIME .Being.dumb...........

REWARD .£.10,0.0.0,0.0.0.......

Make a WANTED poster for a criminal.
It could be someone you know or someone imaginary.
Was their crime against you? Was it something silly?
What's the reward for catching them?

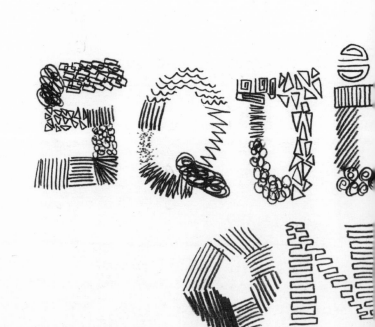

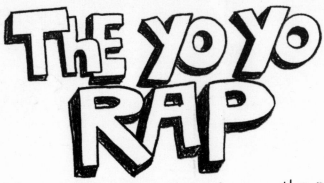

# THE YO YO RAP

Finish writing the 'Yo yo' rap — the most repetitive and annoying rap in the world. Rap it when the 'La la' song gets banned.

Yo yo yo yo yo . . .

my bro

# WRAP
# THIS

Make this page like wrapping paper.

# MUMMIFY THIS

Mummify this page – add bandages.
Use toilet paper or draw them on. Are eyes
peering out or is gunk leaking from between them?

GROAN!

**THESE PAGES ARE YOUR DOORMAT.**
Ask people to wipe their shoes on them on the way in. **NO DOG DOO!**

Whose footprints are whose?
Get everyone to sign their own.

# COME

COME ON IN. MAKE YOURSELF AT HOME.

# GATHER SEEDS, GRAINS, PIPS AND POLLEN HERE:

Wet the page here.
Add mustard seeds.
The seeds will grow if
you keep the page damp.

# SPARE FINGERNAILS

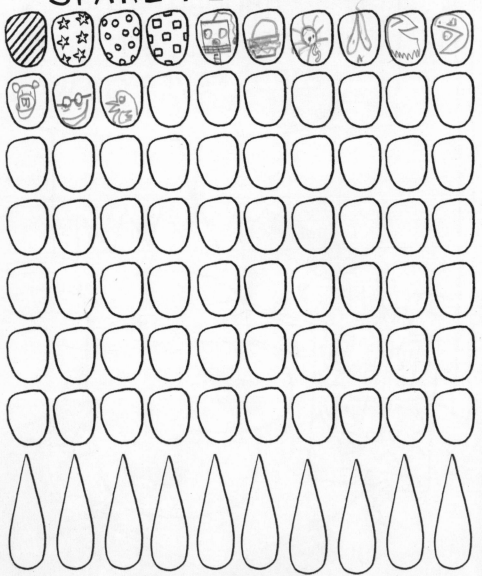

Bling them, paint them or make them dirty and rotten.

THIS PAGE IS YOURS TO
DECORATE

WRITE THE **TRUTH** HERE — WHAT YOU REALLY **THINK** ABOUT SOMETHING:

NOW BURY IT!

# CREATE A MAP SHOWING WHERE THE TRUTH IS BURIED — X MARKS THE SPOT.

Stain your map with coffee or tea to make it look old.

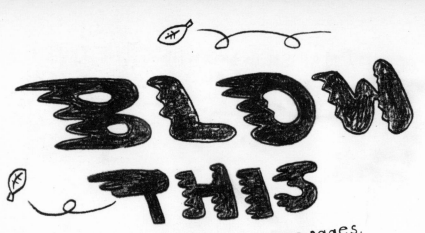

# BLOW THIS

Blow a picture onto these pages.
Use paint and a straw, or a bubble blower, or hang the
book up in the wind with glue on it and see what sticks!

Use this page to be a fan of something you think is GREAT! Celebrate it here! It can be anything you like: a sports team, a celebrity, your mum or dad, a place, or even yourself. Go crazy for it in words, drawings and cutouts.

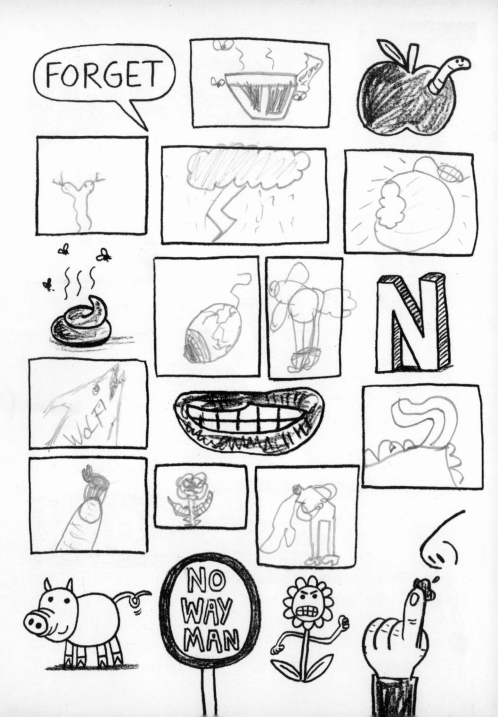

Look carefully at these pages. Close the book then try to recall what's here. How many things can you remember? Add others of your own, then try again a few more times. See how your memory improves!

# THIS IS THE PAGE

Find the word **THE** in magazines and newspapers and collect it here, over and over.

The word **THE** works well because you'll find it lots, but if you'd rather use other words, like DORK, or DOG, or DENDROCHRONOLOGY, go right ahead!

# WATERBOMB!

Start with a square of paper.

1. Fold it in half horizontally, then unfold. Fold in half vertically, then unfold.

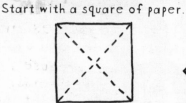

2. Turn it over. Fold it diagonally in both directions, then unfold.

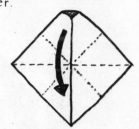

3. Fold the top corner to the bottom. Do not unfold.

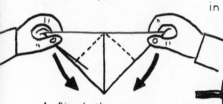

4. Pinch the corners and push them together to look like step 5.

5. Press it flat.

6. Fold the upper layer's corners A and B to point C.

7. Fold the upper layer's side corners D and E to the centre.

8. Tuck the loose top points into the small triangular pockets created in step 7.

9. Turn it over. Repeat steps 6, 7 and 8 for the reverse. It will then will look like this.

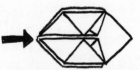

10. Locate the end opening and blow hard into it to inflate.

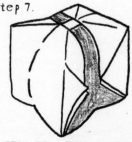

**FILL IT WITH WATER!**

Spill This

Lay a cloth behind this page.

Add spillages and colour. Let them blot. Decorate with stains and dirty finger marks.

# Whatever

you write or draw here

will come TRUE.

S. L. P = Trwe

CRYSTAL BALL

# KEEP A **DAFT DIARY** OF **DUMBNESS** FOR ONE WEEK.

Note down the daft or dumb things you do, see, hear or say during one week — include falling over, forgetfulness and fashion disasters.

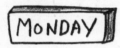

Someone beeped me in a parked car

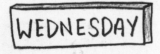

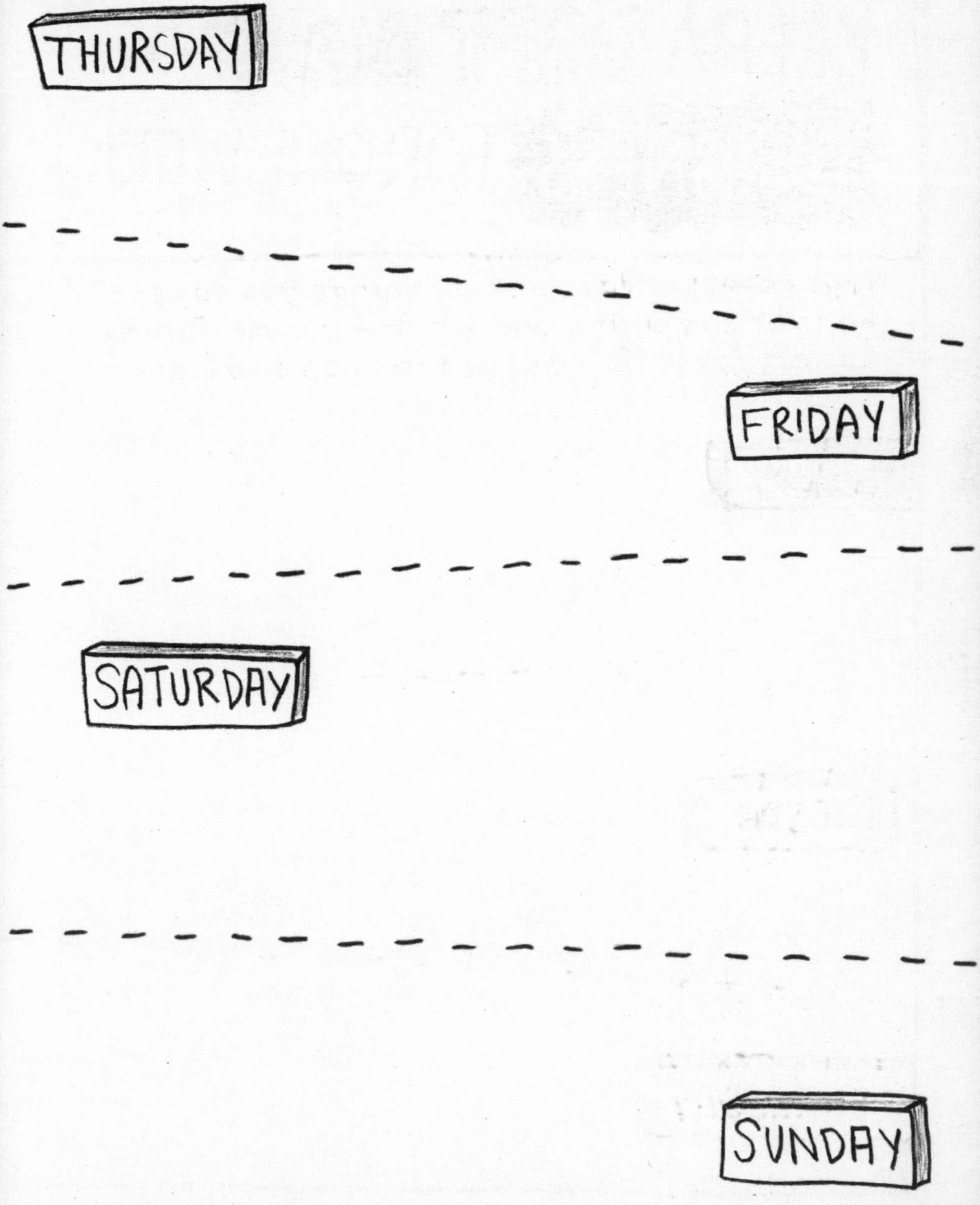

THURSDAY

FRIDAY

SATURDAY

SUNDAY

(Zayan.R.) 76 (mind…)

Eobthm

Yeol

(Tabarek) Tabarek H

(adam)

(Hannah)

↖   ↑   ↑   ↗

Write your signatures here! ⇒

JJ spot! V.G.PS! ✡ ✡
T_T ✎ Kay! V.I.P
Signatures ✎ #Always young!
✡   ✡   ✡ ✡   >_<

TAKE THIS BOOK TO SCHOOL AND GET ALL YOUR FRIENDS TO SIGN THESE PAGES OR WRITE YOU A SHORT MESSAGE - keep these for ever to remember everyone when you are old.

# APPLY A FACE PACK

Face packs might include chocolate, mud, or avocado.

# USE THIS BOOK AS A BAT

How FAR can you bat a ball?
. . . a scrunched-up piece of paper?
. . . a leaf?
. . . a rotten tomato?

How HIGH can you bat a ball?
. . . a feather?
. . . a boiled egg?

How many keepie-uppies
can you do with an apple?

Take the book outdoors.
Challenge a friend to
book baseball or
book table tennis.

TOK

Cover this page in
spirals: long, short,
painted, drawn, stuck
on or cut out.

CRAZY

What's the longest spiral you
can tear? Hang it up.

# REPORT THIS

This is your school report. What would your teachers say about you?

Best teacher is . . . *Miss K* . . . . . . . . . . . . . . . . . . . . .
Teacher you'd most like to gunk is . . . *Miss albans* . . . . . . .

## HAVE YOU EVER . . .
○ Fallen asleep in class?
○ Forgotten your sports kit?
○ Pretended to be sick to try to get a day off?   ○ Copied?
○ Been praised?
◉ Been sent out?
○ Had an 'accident' in class?
◉ Had to hide in the toilets?

## ARE YOU GOOD AT?
◉ Spelling   ○ Making friends
○ Science   ◉ Being on time   ○ Acting
○ Sports   ○ Art   ○ Making people laugh   ◉ Bragging
◉ Maths   ○ Not getting caught   ◉ Music
○ Looking good

### What's your best excuse for not doing your homework?
*wedding eugh*

### What do you think you'll be when you're aged 30?
*Artist*   *Game maker*

# THE WORLD'S WORST PHOTOS

Add the worst photos you can find . . .

# START YOUR OWN COUNTRY.

FIRST, DESIGN YOUR FLAG.

Tape it to a pole.

Write down YOUR rules for YOUR country:

\- - - - - - - - - - - - - - - - - - - - - - - - -

\- - - - - - - - - - - - - - - - - - - - - - - - -

\- - - - - - - - - - - - - - - - - - - - - - - - -

\- - - - - - - - - - - - - - - - - - - - - - - - -

\- - - - - - - - - - - - - - - - - - - - - - - - -

Write down the name of anyone who breaks your
rules and who is banned from your country:

# SWEET WRAPPER ART

Collage sweet wrappers here.
It's a good excuse to eat sweets!

# ROLL THIS INTO A PEA SHOOTER

PHHT

Shoot scrunched-up bits of paper.

MAKE THIS A

# HAIRY PAGE.

Add wool, hair, string, cotton, etc.

Keep adding to this page from one day to the next. Go over things or erase them. It will change as you change your mind. It will never be finished.

# KEEP DOING THIS

# DRAW it LIKE it is

In this book some words are drawn descriptively such as **HEADACHE**, **RUNNY** and **STRIPY**. Try drawing words of your own, or have a go at these: SPLAT, SHATTER, BANG, PRETTY, WOBBLY, SPOTTY, MESSY.

Lean

Splat

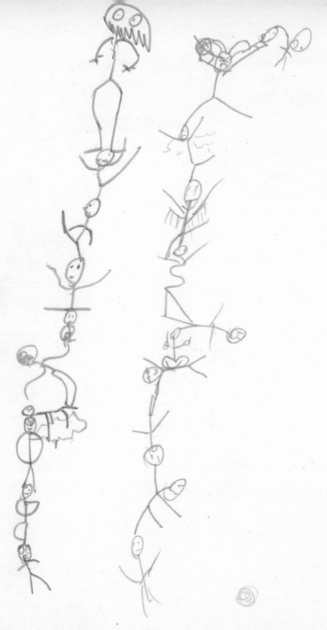

STACK UP STICK MEN

# DRAW HOW YOU'D LOOK AS A FLOWER

# Build it

Design a building that you'd like to live in.

Chocoflat

AN INDOOR FOOTBALL PITCH?!

# CRUMB COLLECTION

Use sticky tape to collect crumbs here.

# NOSE PAINTING

Paint using only your nose. Hold your hands behind your back and get up close: splodge with the tip, smear with the sides.

# AND THE Winner IS...

Colour these rosettes, then award them to your favourite page, your second favourite page and your thirteenth favourite page.

# LISTEN TO THIS...

Ooo baby baby!

Write the lyrics to a song you like. Illustrate them by drawing images the song makes you think of, then decorate them in a style that suits the mood.

# MAKE THIS BOOK . . .

## TALK

Turn any page into a ventriloquist's dummy for a comedy act.

1. Fold a piece of paper in half.

2. Fold it in half again.

3. It should look like this.

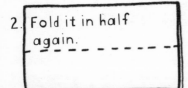

4. Fold it lengthwise to crease it, then unfold.

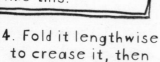

5. Fold the ends to the centre.

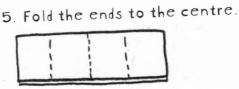

6. It should look like this:

7. Stand it up, with the centre creased, and slide your fingers into the openings at the top and bottom.

8. Draw eyes on or weird features. Decorate as you wish.

# DO THIS WITHOUT MOVING YOUR LIPS:

It's easier to say some words than others. With your mouth a bit open but not moving, say the vowel sounds: A, E, I, O, U. These are easy.

Now try these letter sounds: B, F, V, P, M, W. These are impossible. Ventriloquists switch them: B to D, F to TH, V to TH, P to T, M to N, W to OO.

So 'Bogey' becomes 'Dogey',
'Funny' becomes 'Thunny',
'Very' becomes 'Thery',
'Pick' becomes 'Tick',
'Money' becomes 'Noney',
'Water' becomes 'Ooater'.

The audience don't notice because they're focused on the dummy's moving mouth.

Practise in front of the mirror. Move your dummy's mouth with each syllable.

HEY, WHO YOU CALLING A DUMMY?

# MASH-UP

Combine each pair of pictures to make something funny.

Draw here:

girl's face

custard pie

boy in pants

ants

running man

banana skin

# FEED THIS

Tear a hole here for this mouth. See what weird things you can fit through it: food, paint, objects, words, crayons, pens, magazines, stationery, ideas, anything you want. Note down on this page everything you feed it.

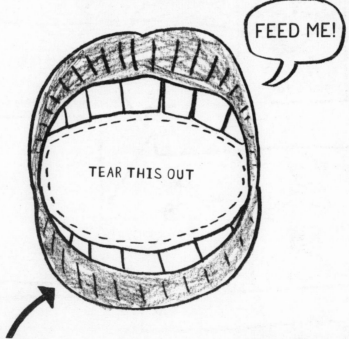

FEED ME!

TEAR THIS OUT

Draw something dribbling from the lips.

DO YOU WANT FRIES WITH THAT?

Everything you fed this book is now being churned up here, in a stomach. How would everything look being mixed up together?

# TAPE THIS

Create a picture here using sticky tape. Pattern the tape or use different colours and widths. Tape objects on or tape over them to make bumps and ridges.

# DESIGN THIS

Design your own **T**-shirt with a slogan.

LIKABOSS

LOOKIN' GOOD

# BLACK AND WHITE

Fill this page with anything that's black and white.
NO COLOUR!

In the two speech bubbles, note down part of a conversation you overhear: people talking in class, at home or on TV. Now look around and draw two random objects you can see, one below each bubble.

## Use this page to communicate your needs for the next hour without speaking.

Hi   *yawn*   Literacy~poop   ?

yolo   what?

OH!   lol   Read Lol !!)!!/!!

Very Sup?

Bored   yo   LOL !!!

*Sopopular   I dont have pix gun

1-2ᵐ till break

yay no 2min!

Scatter things on these pages: cake crumbs, the letters of your name, or anything you feel like. Draw ripples around each thing until they meet and fill the pages.

# DRAW ROUND YOUR LEFT HAND WITH YOUR RIGHT HAND.

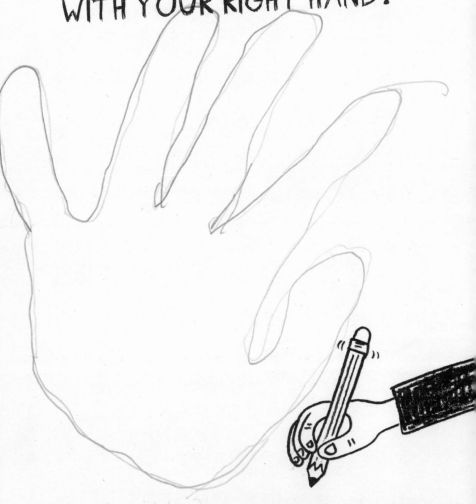

PUT SOMETHING SQUIDGY
NOW CLAP **THE**

# DRAW ROUND YOUR RIGHT HAND WITH YOUR LEFT HAND.

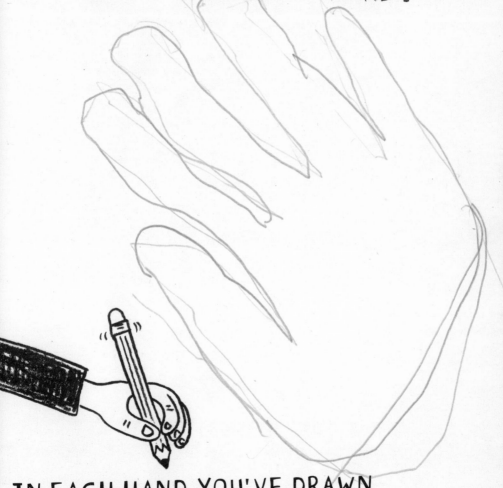

IN EACH HAND YOU'VE DRAWN.
BOOK **TO** SPREAD **IT**.

# THE SPECTRUM

BLINDLY TEAR OLD MAGAZINE PAGES INTO TINY BITS.

Now sort the bits by colour. Paste them here in a spectrum pattern to fill both pages: reds progressing to oranges to yellows to greens to blues to purples.

# SPONGE THIS

Use a sponge to paint.
Smear it, dab it, throw it.

ONE DAY, WHEN YOU BECOME FAMOUS, THIS BOOK OF YOUR DRAWINGS AND THOUGHTS WILL BE WORTH MILLIONS.

Try to sell this page cheaply now to someone, explaining that it's a good investment. Draw something they might like: ask them their favourite colours and use those, or draw a picture of them. Sign it and swap it for cash – even just one penny proves you can turn your ideas into money.

# One minute...GO!

You have just one minute to draw each thing below as many times as you can:

Star

Stick man

Tree

Spider

Mouse

Cat

Beast

Vehicle

Building

QUIT DAWDLING, DORK!

0:59

Trap

Invention

# THINK OF A ROOM THAT
# YOU'RE NOT IN NOW.
# TRY TO DRAW IT FROM MEMORY.

Go and check how you did.

Now redecorate and fill the room to make it **MUCH MORE EXCITING**.

# TO REMEMBER A RAINY DAY.

Colour a picture of anything you can see out of the window. Take it outside in the rain so the colours run. Leave it to dry.

TRY TO RIP THIS PAGE

INTO NINE AND A HALF PIECES

# NOTICE This...

Make a notice that's so bright and bold EVERYONE will notice it. It could be an announcement, a slogan, a message, an advert or just a word.

Save this page for a special moment:
for when you are feeling inspired, or when
you are incredibly bored. Or for when you
really want to do something in this book again.

# MEASURE THIS

HOW TALL IS THIS BOOK? ...............

HOW TALL ARE YOU? ...............

HOW HEAVY IS THIS BOOK? ...............

HOW HEAVY ARE YOU? ...............

HOW MANY PEOPLE HAVE HELD IT? ...............

HOW MANY PEOPLE'S NAMES ARE IN IT? ...............

HOW MUCH DID IT COST? ...............

HOW MUCH DO YOU EARN? ...............

HOW FAR HAS IT TRAVELLED? ...............

HOW MANY PAGES ARE IN IT? ...............

HOW MANY PAGES HAVE YOU DONE? ...............

HOW LONG HAVE YOU HAD IT? ...............

HOW FAR CAN YOU THROW IT? ...............

HOW MANY OF YOUR THOUGHTS ARE IN IT? ...............

HOW MANY OF YOUR FRIENDS HAVE SEEN IT? ...............

HOW COOL IS IT? ...............

HOW COOL ARE YOU? ...............

HOW OFTEN ARE YOU IN TROUBLE? ...............

HOW UNFAIR IS THAT? ...............

While you're thinking, colour in all the 'O's above.

# COLOUR THESE!

# MAKE THEM ALL DIFFERENT.

# SAUCE ART

Make a ketchup painting — or brown sauce,
or mustard, if you prefer.

# IT POOED ON THIS!

An enormous hungry beast has eaten everything in the art shop: pens, paints, paper, crayons — everything!

What would this page look like if it pooed on it?

OH, MAN!

Describe or draw
what happened on
these great days:

The day you won a gold medal.

The day you were on TV.

The day you pooped ur pants.

Describe or draw
what happened on
these terrible days:

# IMAGINARY
## PERSONAL DISASTERS

OOPS!

The day you threw up in class.

The day you forgot your clothes.

The day you barfed inside

# SHARE THIS

Get as many people as you can to draw on these pages, all at once, until they're full.

# ARGUE FIERCELY

Select two different art tools, such as a pen and a paintbrush. Make them argue with each other in marks and scribbles. Draw the noise and the shouting.

GRRR!

# HOLD THIS

Make a holder for pens, art materials or even liquid.
It won't last long with liquid in it — and don't drink
from it if you've painted it beforehand.

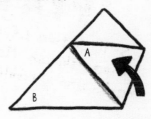

1. Decorate a square, about 15cm across. Place it decorated side down.

2. Fold it into a triangle with the decorated side visible.

3. Fold corner 'A' to its opposite edge, meeting it at about 90°.

4. Fold the top corner of the front layer downwards.

5. Turn it all over and, on the reverse, fold corner 'B' upwards to its opposite edge.

6. Also on the reverse, fold down the top corner of the remaining layer.

7. Use your fingers to open up the holder. Fill it.

# CLASH THIS

Draw or cut out things that clash and combine them in a picture – things that DON'T belong together.

# LAYER THIS

Tear junk mail into large pieces.

Paste them over this page, layer upon layer.

Now tear strips away to look like

layers of old adverts on a billboard.

# SHOOTING GALLERY

Take the book outdoors and paint these pages
using a water pistol and water-based paint.
Involve a friend if you want — for a 'shoot off'.

# THE SAD PAGE

This page is for your sad thoughts.
Decorate them to cheer them up.
Use it as a tissue for tears.

# PICK AN EVENT THAT HAPPENED TO YOU. TURN IT INTO A NEWS STORY WITH A HEADLINE AND A PICTURE.

Name of newspaper:

**BORING NEWS!**

Headline:

**GUY FARTSON QUEEN**

What happened:

Photo:

# DESIGN THREE BOOKMARKS.
Mark where you are in the book,
the most revolting page and the silliest page.

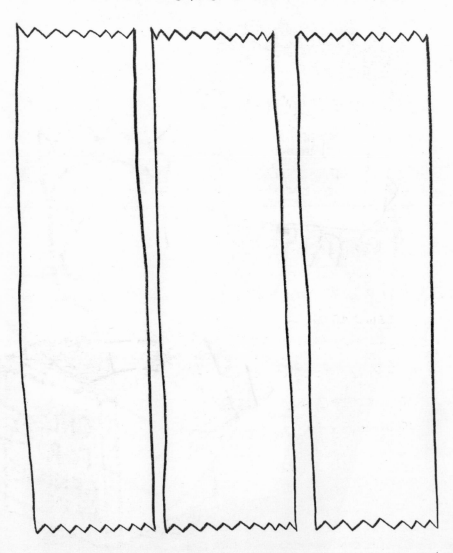

Make a new cover for this book and glue
it on the back. Call it anything you want.
Be the author if you like.

Turn the book back to front
and upside down to switch
between the two covers.
Convince people
you are reading
something different.

# EXAMINE

# THESE

Can you spot the difference between these pictures?
(Answer on the last page.)

Things to release onto these pages might include:
a pet cat with dirty paws, a dog, the dog's fleas,
your burps, your frustration, your imagination.

# A BOW-TIE A DAY
# FOR A WEEK

### Refine them.
### Design your own
### the way you like
### to wear them.

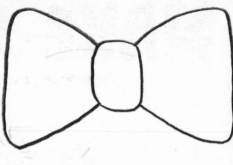

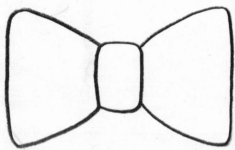

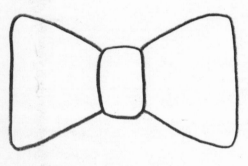

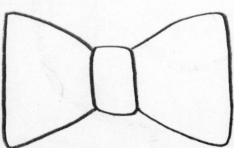

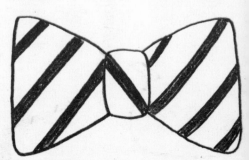

# MAKE-UP THIS

Add war paint or make-up.

OR ZOMBIE MAKE-UP!

Make these pages gross.
What looks gross to you?

# PERFORM THIS

Magic torn paper back together again!

Back of sheet 2

Start with two plain identical sheets of paper (sheet 1 and sheet 2).

Scrunch sheet 1 into a ball. Hold it behind the top corner of sheet 2 with your left hand. Show sheet 2 to the audience and say, 'I will rip up this sheet of paper then magic it back together.'

With your right hand, tear sheet 2 to pieces. Pass each loose piece to your left hand, keeping them in front of the screwed-up ball of sheet 1.

Now scrunch the loose pieces forwards to create a second ball in front of the ball you've been hiding.

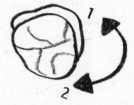

Holding the two balls together, turn them round as you blow on them and say a magic word: 'Abracadidiot!'

Hold up both balls again, now with ball 1 at the front. Slowly unfold it, keeping the ripped ball 2 hidden behind. Hey presto – the paper appears intact again!

THIS CREASES ME UP!

Back of sheet 1 unfolding

# MELT IT

Choose any object that you like the look of.
Draw it as if it was melting.

HELP, I'M MELTING!

# LET'S  ABOUT ME

| What I think about me. | What other people think about me. |
|---|---|
| Funny | Dunno  |

Start a band. Think of a name for it.
Make a poster advertising your first big concert.

If people turn up and you don't
know how to play any instruments,
just act cool and say the
band has had to split because
of 'artistic differences'.

# RECORD THE SOUNDS YOU CAN MAKE WITH THIS PAGE OR BOOK.

CRUMPLE

RUSTLE

RRRIIIIIIIIPP!

WHACK!

## you are a stinky cucumber

What are most ridiculous phrases you can make using these words?

lice boyfriend amazing break bad answer
my pie six pick whatever runs wash bald
scab burps cats fish sausage that boring has
what squidgy of brilliant green house boy
chocolate are rat bottom face a burst you
lemons hairy squashes elephant banana fluff
wet monster electric dad haunted never with
pants like mouldy fire prince their bears
happy exploded are ate bendy her did scary
spot not are liquidized toffee of so my you
a rules robber your like going my toilet on
I alone trouble afraid all and fairies there
is in big up I your gross like jelly made poo
a pulsating berserk went large are the brain
being fantastic pig suck an my day dream a
I and naked our the of he by hit it girl a
a leg gorilla sore mum am has a a are the
a trousers dog on is is

Rearrange the words into
ridiculous phrases here:

Gather barcodes from packaging. Combine them here in a design.

# CLONE THIS

Draw in multiple colours by holding coloured
pencils or felt-tipped pens in a bunch.
Sign this page in mutliple too.

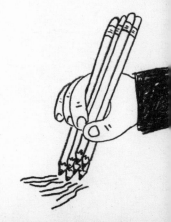

# INJURE THIS

How might this page look if it was injured? Perhaps something would be oozing from it, or would it have a huge scab on it? It may look broken, bruised, stung or scarred. It may need plasters. You choose.

A BOOK ATTACKED ME.

# THIS ISN'T A NUMBER 8

It's part of something else. **YOU** decide what it is.

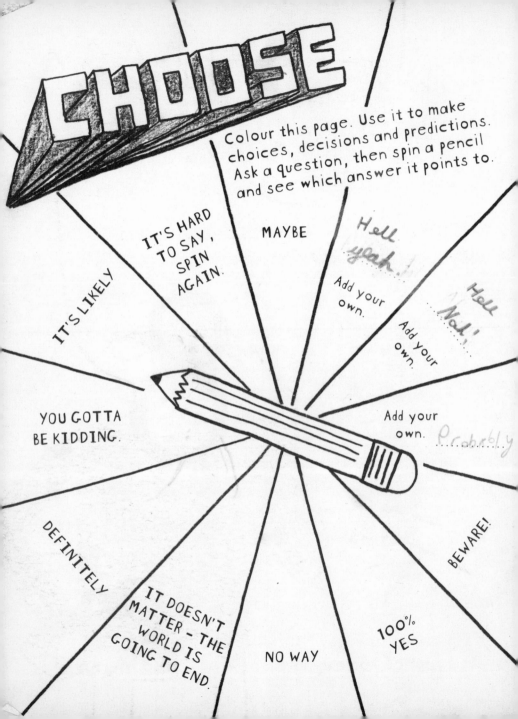

# THIS IS A STICK-UP!

Colour these. Stick or tape them where you like.

THIS IS A **SIGN** OF THINGS TO COME →

IF YOU'RE READING THIS, THEN YOU'RE A _todd man._

HANDS OFF

LOOK BEHIND YOU

Temporary SIGN

! LOSER

SPLAT

OOPPS

# RUB THIS OUT

Cover this page in pencil. Use an eraser
to draw or write a ghostly message.

# Mini MASTERPIECES

Search through this book for mini masterpieces
hidden within your pictures. Find small sections
to cut out and hang here in your gallery,
or draw new ones. Hold a mini exhibition.

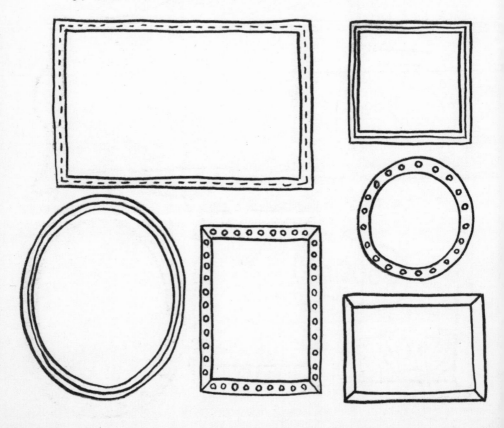

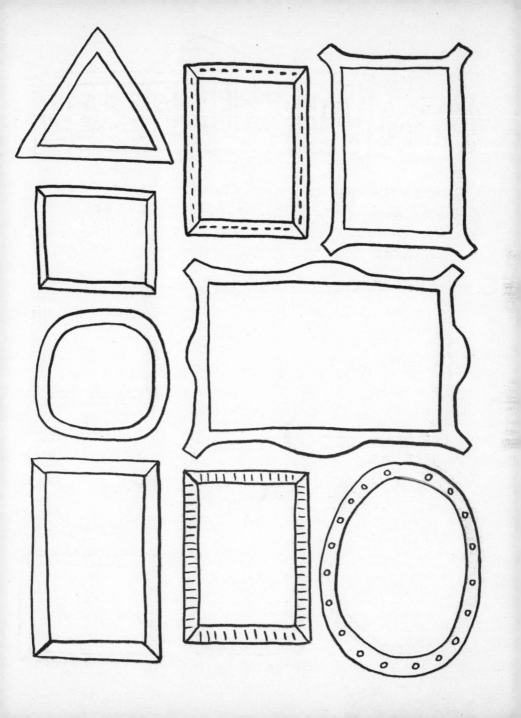

# BACK TO Front

Stick notes onto your face with words on them that describe you. Now draw yourself in the mirror.

# THIS IS MAGIC

Fairies go here.
Slam the book shut to squish them.

# END THIS BOOK

## IN ANY WAY YOU WANT . . .

with a bang